This book belongs to:

Name:.....Sarah...Connolly.....

Age:...8............................

I live in a place called:

61....Coler...glen....Road.......

Editor: Lisa Carless **Designer:** Colin Treanor
© Disney. Based on the Pooh stories by A.A. Milne. © The Pooh Properties Trust.
All rights reserved. Published in Great Britain in 2005 by Egmont Books Limited,
239 Kensington High Street, London W8 6SA. Printed in Italy. ISBN 1 4052 2100 3
3 5 7 9 10 8 6 4 2

Hello, everyone!

Welcome to the Hundred Acre Wood with Winnie the Pooh and all his friends. Why don't you join in the fun and games? There's so much to do!

We've hidden lots of little objects in your annual – see how many you can find of each one, and write the numbers in the boxes. Have fun finding them!

Contents

The reward

1 One sunny day, Pooh decided to visit his friend Tigger. "Tigger is always good fun," said Pooh. But Tigger wasn't at home or in any of his usual places.

2 "Tigger!" called Pooh, as he wandered around the Hundred Acre Wood. But there was no reply from his bouncy buddy.

3 Pooh started getting worried and went to see Piglet. "Tigger is lost and I don't know what to do," gulped Pooh.

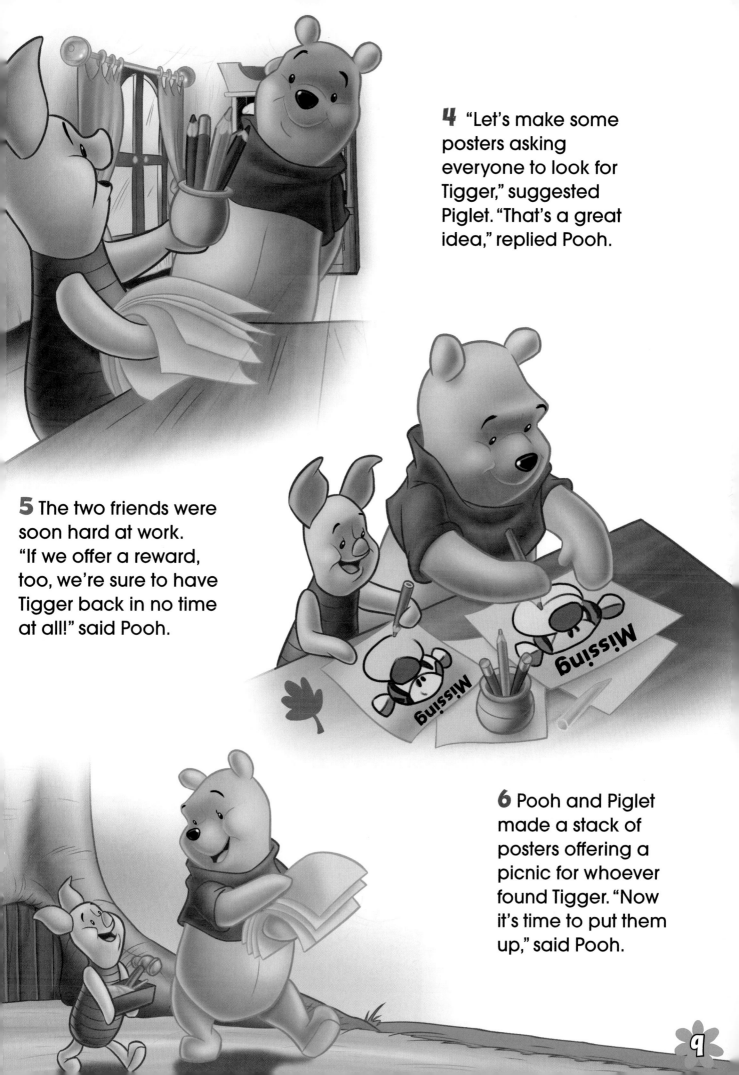

4 "Let's make some posters asking everyone to look for Tigger," suggested Piglet. "That's a great idea," replied Pooh.

5 The two friends were soon hard at work. "If we offer a reward, too, we're sure to have Tigger back in no time at all!" said Pooh.

6 Pooh and Piglet made a stack of posters offering a picnic for whoever found Tigger. "Now it's time to put them up," said Pooh.

7 Pooh and Piglet dashed around the Hundred Acre Wood, fixing the posters on to trees. "Make sure they're hammered in properly," said Piglet.

8 The sound of the hammering woke up Tigger, who had been happily snoozing in the long, summer grass. "Boy, that was a super nap!" yawned Tigger.

9 Tigger soon noticed the posters with his picture dotted around the Wood. "Fancy that! My buddies are searching for me!" he chuckled.

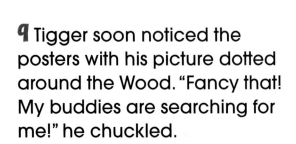

10 Tigger took a poster and headed straight to Pooh's house. "I've found me!" giggled Tigger.

11 Pooh and Piglet were so pleased to see Tigger again, they gave him the reward! "A picnic isn't a picnic unless you share it with your friends," cheered Tigger.

Summer fun

1

Choose three of Eeyore's flowers and copy them carefully into these boxes. Count the petals and make sure you draw the right number!

2 Draw in the missing branches and leaves of the tree.

3 Copy the patterns and the colours to finish the butterflies.

13

Piglet's colouring pages

Use your favourite pens to add some colour to this scene. Look at the little picture to help you choose.

1 How many paper aeroplanes are there?

2 Who has the largest aeroplane?

3 Which aeroplane is the highest?

4 Can you find three butterflies?

Pooh's Heffalump MOVIE

Deep in the Hundred Acre Wood, the day started like any other. The sun smiled down, the Wood was quiet, and honey flowed from hives. Yes, it was a day like any other . . . except that a visitor had come to the Hundred Acre Wood.

Strange, frightening, and very large tracks trailed through the trees and a strange sound woke Pooh, Piglet, Tigger and Roo.

"Mama!" cried Roo, hopping to the window. "Did you hear that sound?"

Kanga picked up her son to look out of the window with him. "What sort of sound, dear?" she asked.

"I don't know," Roo told her. "It was sort of strange - and kind of neat!"

Suddenly, Pooh, Piglet and Tigger rushed past Roo's window.

"Good morning, Pooh!" Roo called.

"Oh, I wish it was a good morning," Pooh answered. "Oh, bother."

"What's happened?" Roo called. "Where's everybody going?"

"To Rabbit's house," Piglet told him. "He'll know what to do. I hope."

Everyone was very pleased to find that Rabbit was all right and, one by one, they each told their stories of how the loud noise woke them up.

Then, Roo noticed something.

"Hey, I've found a footprint!" he said.

Tigger chuckled. "Oh, that's impossibibble."

Rabbit then suggested that the footprint could belong to a heffalump.

Rabbit led them to the very edge of the Hundred Acre Wood.

"They live right over there," Rabbit whispered. "Heffalump Hollow." Then Rabbit and Tigger told scary stories about heffalumps. They said they were big and wide and very, very mean.

That gave Roo an idea. "Let's go get them!" he said. He said that it would be a grand thing to be the first to catch a heffalump.

"Come back with your equipment and I'll show you all how it's done," said Rabbit.

When everyone returned, none of the equipment was what Rabbit had in mind.

"I brought some rope!" said Roo, helpfully. "C'mon everybody! Let's go get 'em!"

"Ah, just a moment, Roo. It's too dangerous. You're too young. You could get hurt," said Rabbit.

"You mean . . . I can't go?" asked Roo.

"I'm sorry, Roo," said Rabbit.

Roo heard his mother calling. Then he heard Rabbit tell the others, "All right, everyone, we'll meet here tomorrow for the grand expedition."

Sadly, Roo headed for home.

That night, Roo practised with his rope. "I could capture a heffalump just as good as anybody," he mumbled to himself. "I just know I could."

Roo hopped over to his mother. "They've got six heads full of big sharp teeth and a big old spiky tail that can crush a house all at once!"

"My, my," said Kanga.

"And everyone's gonna catch one but me. It isn't fair," added Roo, sadly.

"I'm grown up enough to catch a heffalump, aren't I, Mum?"

"How about starting with a good night's sleep?" Kanga replied, as she tucked Roo into bed and left him dreaming of heffalump hunts.

Early the next morning, Roo made up his mind. If the others would not let him go on their heffalump hunt, he would go on his own. Roo took his rope and a bag with his lunch and crept out of his house. He found the heffalump tracks and studied them for a minute. Then, he set off for Heffalump Hollow.

Pooh, Piglet, Eeyore and Tigger were getting ready for their expedition, too.

"A perfect morning for catching heffalumps!" said Rabbit. He marched his group to the edge of their safe wood, and led the way to Heffalump Hollow.

Roo had entered Heffalump Hollow, too. He moved quietly, trying to be brave. As Roo edged forward, a long trunk sniffed the air behind him. When Roo set down his lunch, the trunk snaked out! Soon, all of Roo's lunch had disappeared!

"Who . . . who's there?" called Roo. He followed the trail of lunch crumbs to an old mill. Taking a deep breath, Roo pushed open the door and tip-toed inside. Suddenly, a trunk tapped Roo.

"You're it!" called a voice.

"Aaaaah!" Roo screamed.

All Roo could see was a dark shape with a long trunk. "Now you've got to catch me!" The dark shape laughed.

Roo looked for a way past the shape. "Uh, I have to leave." he said, then raced for the door.

The shape blocked his way. "But you've got to catch me now," said. "Don't you want to play?"

"I can't," said Roo. "Because I've got to catch a heffalump."

The shape squealed for joy and tackled Roo. They tumbled out of the mill and into the bright sunlight. "You can catch me! I'm a heffalump!"

Roo stared at the heffalump. He didn't look anything like Rabbit's description. "If you're a heffalump," said Roo, "where are your horns and spiky tail?"

"I don't know," said the heffalump.

Roo thought about that. "Are you sure you're a heffalump?" he asked.

"My mum says I am," he replied.

That was good enough for Roo. As he threw his rope over the heffalump, he cried, "In the name of the Hundred Acre Wood, I capture you!"

"You've got to come with me, now," added Roo.

"Why?" asked the heffalump.

"Because I captured you and . . . because I'm a grown-up," Roo announced.

"Wow! You must have your own call then," said the heffalump, as he tried to trumpet. It sounded more like a wheeze! "I haven't found mine yet. My mum said I'd find it when I grow up," he added.

Just then, Roo heard the same sort of trumpeting he'd heard yesterday morning.

"Gotta go! That's my mum," said the heffalump.

"Don't go yet! Let's go see my friends, then you can go back to your mummy," said Roo.

"Well, OK. I guess," said the heffalump, trotting along beside Roo. "My name is Heffridge Trumpler Brompe Heffalump, the Fourth. Everybody calls me Lumpy. What's your name?"

"My name's Roo," replied Roo.

Meanwhile, elsewhere in the wood, the others were having a lot of success capturing . . . each other!

When Roo and Lumpy reached the fence, Lumpy stopped.

"I'm not supposed to go into that part of the woods. Scary things live there," said Lumpy, as he peered through the fence.

Roo laughed. "That's where I live. There aren't any scary things there," he said.

"There are, too," Lumpy insisted. "There's a stripy thing that bounces and it goes 'Hoo-hoo-HOO!' Then it pounces!"

"No, no. That's Tigger. He's great!" Roo climbed the fence.

Roo looked into the Hundred Acre Wood that was so safe and dear to him. How could Lumpy be afraid? Climbing through the fence, he looked back at Lumpy. "There's nothing scary here."

"Promise?" said Lumpy.

"Promise," said Roo, helping Lumpy through the fence.

Back in Heffalump Hollow, Rabbit was yelling at everyone.

"No more fun and games! The heffalump is all but in our grasp!" he shouted. Rabbit was more right than he knew. A real heffalump trumpeted close by!

Suddenly, Piglet saw bushes shaking.

"It's coming!" he squeaked. "It's coming!"

They didn't realise it was only Eeyore, stepping out of the bushes!

"I'm afraid to ask," muttered Eeyore.

Roo was surprised that the Hundred Acre Wood was so quiet. He and Lumpy stopped at Pooh's house first.

"It looks like nobody's home," said Roo.

Lumpy's tummy growled. "Sorry," he said. "My mummy usually makes me a snack about now." And before Roo could stop him, Lumpy was eating Pooh's honey!

"Oh, well, I guess he won't mind," said Roo.

As they left, they accidentally slammed Pooh's door and pots of honey smashed to the floor.

"Uh, oh," said Roo and Lumpy.

They hurried on to Rabbit's garden. Roo looked around. "They must still be out on the expedition," he said.

Soon, he and Lumpy were racing through Rabbit's neat rows, playing catch and every other game that neat gardens weren't meant for. By the time they were done, Rabbit's garden was a fruit and vegetable mess.

"Uh, oh," said Roo and Lumpy.

"We'd better get cleaned up," said Roo. He led Lumpy to the stream and showed him how to make the biggest splash.

Lumpy showed Roo how to spray out water. He gave his friend a nice cool shower.

Roo and Lumpy decided it was time to race some clouds. Lumpy held out his rope so Roo could lead him, but Roo didn't take it. Lumpy had become his friend.

"Lumpy," said Roo, "you're not captured any more." Roo untied the rope and threw it aside.

Lumpy laughed and the two ran off for more fun.

As Roo and Lumpy skipped off, Pooh, Piglet, Tigger and Rabbit dashed home.

"Well," gasped Rabbit, "all in all, a successful heffalump expedition."

Pooh thought about that. "Are you sure, Rabbit?" asked Pooh.

"Well, certainly!" said Rabbit. "Just look around. You don't see any heffalumps, do you?"

That was when they noticed the tracks leading to Pooh and Rabbit's houses.

They soon found the broken honeypots in Pooh's house and then they found Rabbit's garden with all of its squashed and eaten fruit and vegetables.

Tigger, Roo, and Piglet ran in panicky circles.

Rabbit stopped them. "That's it!" he said. "We need traps. Everywhere!"

No one was very sure how to build a heffalump trap so they used everything: a cage, a net, a mattress, a pulley, pots and pans, an iron, a hidden hole, and of course, some honey for bait. They hammered and sawed and wheelbarrelled and bounced until finally, they all stood back from their finished traps.

"Behold!" said Tigger. "A super-duper-extralooper, hunka hunka heffa-trap!"

Lumpy and Roo were still playing when they heard Lumpy's mother call from far away.

"I really have to go," said Lumpy. "She sounds worried."

"Come on," said Roo. "I'll help you find her."

Lumpy was right. His mama was worried about him. She had found his tracks at the mill, but she couldn't find her son. And while Mama Heffalump looked for Lumpy, Kanga began looking for Roo.

Roo called out for Lumpy's mother, but they seemed to be getting farther away instead of closer.

"I want my mum," said Lumpy.

"Me, too," said Roo, miserably.

That was it! "My mum!" cried Roo. "She'll know what to do! Come on, Lumpy, let's go back and find her."

Roo soon spotted his friends and they spotted him and the heffalump!

For a second, no one moved. Then everyone but Kanga began waving and shouting.

"It's got Roo!" shouted Rabbit.

"Stop him!" yelled Tigger.

A heffalump trap clanged and snapped at Lumpy. Terrified, Lumpy ran away.

"Lumpy! Wait!" cried Roo, racing after him. When Roo caught up to Lumpy, his friend was trapped in a cage.

"You said they wouldn't be scary," Lumpy sobbed. "You promised."

"Oh, Lumpy," said Roo, "I'm so sorry." Roo tried to free his friend, but he wasn't strong enough.

He could hear Rabbit and the others calling for him. Looking up, Roo saw a big knot tying the cage together.

Roo hopped to the top of the cage. He worked on the knot until it came loose. The cage fell apart and Lumpy was free! Lumpy helped Roo down.

Just then, Kanga and the others found Roo. "The heffalump's got him!" cried Pooh.

"Drop my little bouncin' buddy, you heffaly-rascalump!" called Tigger. Swinging their lassos, Rabbit, Pooh, Piglet and Tigger ran to rescue Roo. Kanga tried to stop them, but four lassos fell on Lumpy.

"No!" shouted Roo.

His friends stopped in surprise.

"Let him go!" Roo told them. "You're scaring him! Heffalumps are not big and scary! Lumpy's my friend." Roo patted Lumpy. "He's just a kid like me."

25

Roo could see that his friends didn't understand. He had to convince them.

"He gets afraid," Roo told Piglet. "And he likes honey," Roo told Pooh. "And he's even learning how to bounce," he told Tigger.

One by one, Piglet, Pooh, and Tigger let go of their ropes.

Only Rabbit's rope was left.

"You've go to uncapture him!" said Roo. "You've got to!"

Finally, Rabbit let his rope drop, too.

Lumpy backed away from Roo's scary friends. Behind him was a steep slope. Before he knew it, he was falling!

Roo grabbed one of the ropes to help his friend. He stopped Lumpy, but Roo sailed downward instead. He landed in a deep hole.

"Hold on, Roo!" called Lumpy. "I have an idea!" Lumpy ran to the edge of the wood and lifted his trunk. "TAROOT! TAROOT!" Lumpy had found his call!

Deep in the wood, another trumpet answered Lumpy. "Mummy!" cried Lumpy. "Don't worry, Roo. My mummy's coming."

Mama Heffalump crashed into the clearing looking angry.

"Heffridge Trumpler Brompet Heffalump the Fourth! Where have you been?" she said. Then she pulled her son into a tight hug. "Oh, my little darlin', I've been worried sick."

Lumpy wiggled free. "I'm OK, Mummy, but my friend, Roo's in trouble."

"Roo," Mama Heffalump shouted, "can you hear me, love? Now don't be frightened. I'm Lumpy's mummy. Just leave it to me."

Carefully, Mama Heffalump pulled the heavy logs away from Roo. Rabbit and the others watched in amazement.

"Easy does it," said Mama Heffalump. She picked up Roo with her trunk and gently held him out to Kanga. Kanga held Roo close.

"Oh, Roo! I was so worried!" Kanga said.

Lumpy snuggled in to his mother, too. "You did it!" He trumpeted happily.

"Oh, Lumpy," said Mama Heffalump, "you found your call."

"Well, would ya look at that?" said Tigger. "Heffalumps don't have spikety tails, after all."

"Oh, Rabbit," Pooh said, "that's why the heffalump was in our wood. She was looking for her baby."

Now that the adventure was over, everyone knew it was time for the heffalumps to go home. But Lumpy and Roo weren't ready.

The two mothers looked at each other and laughed. They couldn't resist allowing the new friends to spend a little more time together.

As Pooh and the gang watched, they realised they were delighted to have the heffalumps as their new friends.

Paint with Lumpy

Can you help Lumpy to match these paint pots into pairs? Which coloured pot doesn't have a match?

Answers: The purple pot doesn't have a match.

28

Lumpy is about to do some drawing and painting. He's going to draw and then colour in the tree in the distance. Would you like to help him?

Lumpy's colouring page

Solve the sums

Can you solve the sums on Lumpy's balloons?

a 3 + 2

b 2 + 2

c 5 + 2

d 6 + 1

e 7 + 3

Write your answers here.

a ☐ b ☐ c ☐

d ☐ e ☐

Which sum total is the largest?
Which is the smallest?

Piglet's colour race

Play this fun colouring game with a friend. Who will be the first to colour in their picture of Piglet?

You will need: a dice and coloured pens for each player.

Player 1

32

How to play: Decide who will be Player 1 and who will be Player 2. Take it in turns to roll the dice and colour in a section of your drawing that matches the number on your dice. If all the sections with that number are already coloured in, wait until your next turn to try again. The first player to complete their picture is the winner!

Player 2

33

Which wellies?

Eeyore needs a matching welly for each foot. Which colour should he choose?

Answer: Blue.

Learn to draw Pooh

1 Colour this picture of Pooh.

2 Carefully trace over the blue lines to draw Pooh. Copy his face from picture 1.

3 Draw the same lines you drew in picture 2 to finish Pooh. The outline will help you.

4 Now you're ready to draw and colour Pooh all by yourself. Use the other pictures to help you.

Fun and more fun

1 Look at picture a and draw in the things that are missing on picture b.

2 Draw a line to match each group of bees to the right number.

1 2 3 4 5 6

 36

Eeyore's quiet friends

1 One warm, sunny day, Eeyore was quietly wandering along. He was feeling rather hot and tired, when he saw some cocoons hanging from a branch.

2 "You look nice and cool hanging there. I think I'll stay with you for a while," sighed Eeyore and he moved into the shade.

3 Eeyore felt unusually happy just resting quietly under the tree with his silent little companions. But then, Eeyore heard a loud cawing sound.

4 A group of hungry crows had spotted the cocoons and were swooping down to peck them off the branches.

5 Eeyore swished his tail as hard as he could and scared the crows away. "Don't worry, cocoons. Nothing will happen to you while you're with me," said Eeyore.

Suddenly, the cocoons began to wriggle and split open. Eeyore gasped, as dazzling butterflies began to emerge.

7 Before long, a cloud of rainbow-coloured butterflies were fluttering all around Eeyore. "Now my kind little friends' wings will keep me cool in the sunshine," chuckled Eeyore.

Tidying time

1 Can you find a pair of green and yellow socks in Roo's untidy room?

2 Now look at the things on Roo's floor and find four matching pairs.

Answers: 1) The socks are at the end of Roo's bed; 2) a + h; b + l; f + i; g + j.

# Tigger's colouring page

Pooh's day

Seven o'clock

The sun is shining.
It's time to . . .

Nine o'clock

Tuck in, Pooh.
It's time for . . .

Ten o'clock

Learning is fun!
It's time to . . .

play   get up   lunch

42

What does Pooh do at these times during the day? Look at the words at the bottom of the page and copy them into the right box.

Twelve o'clock

Pooh's hungry.
It's time for . . .

Three o'clock

Whee! How fast can you go? It's time to . . .

Eight o'clock

Snuggle up in bed.
It's time to . . .

sleep   study   breakfast

Going home game

Play this fun game with your friends.
Who will reach Pooh's house first?

1

2

3

4 Miss a go to help Eeyore find his tail.

5

19 Rabbit gives you a ride in his wheelbarrow to space 24.

18

17 Rabbit talks for ages – miss a go.

16

15

20

21

22

23 Honey gives you energy – forward 5 spaces.

24

25

Take-away pots

How many pots do Pooh and Tigger have altogether?

 takes  How many pots are left?

 takes  How many pots are left now?

 takes  How many pots are left for Pooh now?

Answers: Pooh and Tigger started off with 12 pots. After Tigger took 3 pots, there were 9 pots left. After Roo took 2, there were 7 pots left. After Piglet took 4, Pooh is left with 3 pots.

2 3 4 5 6 7 8 9 10 11 12

Spring cleaning

1 It was a sunny spring day and Roo was ready to go outside to play. "You can't go out until you've done some spring cleaning," said Kanga.

2 "Aww, I'll miss all the fun in the sunshine," grumbled Roo, as he trudged into his untidy room. "You'll be glad you did it when it's finished," replied Kanga.

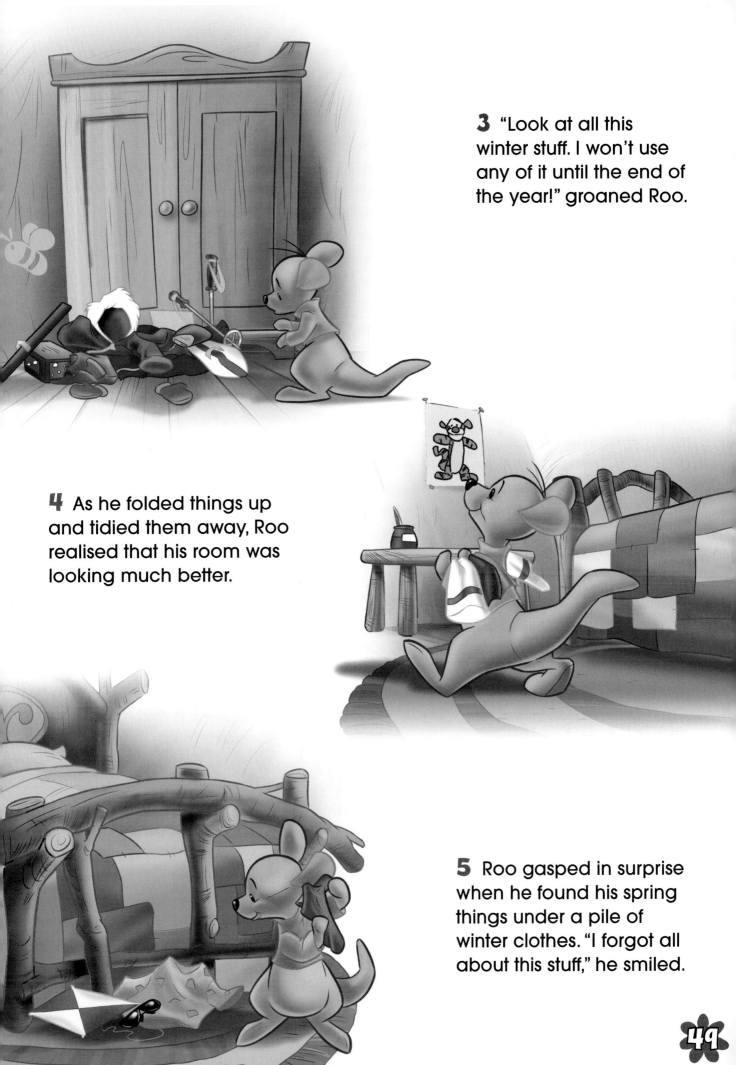

3 "Look at all this winter stuff. I won't use any of it until the end of the year!" groaned Roo.

4 As he folded things up and tidied them away, Roo realised that his room was looking much better.

5 Roo gasped in surprise when he found his spring things under a pile of winter clothes. "I forgot all about this stuff," he smiled.

6 Kanga was
very impressed
when she saw how clean
and tidy the room was. "Well done, Roo!
Now you can go out and play," said Kanga.

7 "You were right, Mum
I am glad I did the sprin
cleaning, because now
have all this great stuff t
play with," cheered Roo

The right one

Pooh wants the honey, Rabbit wants the carrot and Eeyore wants a tasty thistle. Who will get what they want?

Answer: Rabbit.

51

What is it?

Rabbit has drawn one of his favourite things. Join the dots from 1 to 20 to see what it is.

52

Answer: A watering can

Piglet's colouring pages

A pebble caterpillar

Here's how to make a colourful caterpillar.

You will need:
pebbles
paint
brushes

1 Collect six or seven smooth pebbles of different sizes.

2 Wash and dry them well with kitchen paper.

3 Paint the pebbles different colours and leave them to dry.

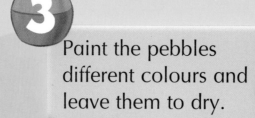

4 Arrange the pebbles in a line, the biggest at the front, the smallest at the back.

5 Paint a caterpillar head and front legs on the big pebble and a pattern on the rest of the stones.

See how many different patterns you can create!

All change

1 One morning, Piglet woke up ready for another fun-filled summer day. But the sun was still low in the sky! Piglet looked at his clock. "It says it's time to get up," he puzzled.

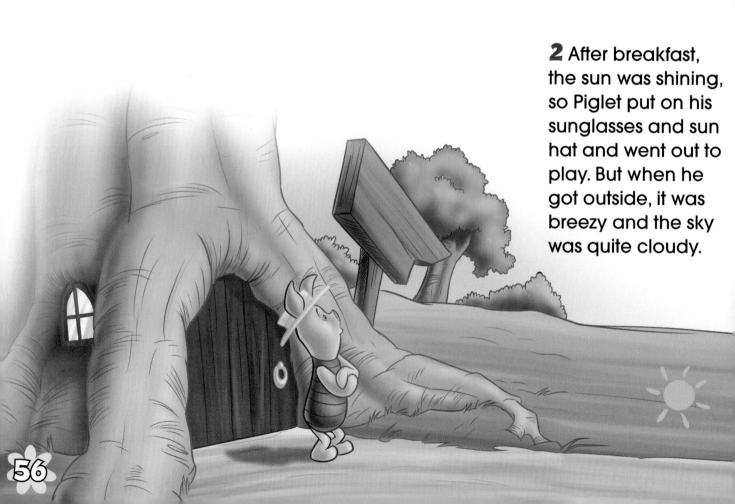

2 After breakfast, the sun was shining, so Piglet put on his sunglasses and sun hat and went out to play. But when he got outside, it was breezy and the sky was quite cloudy.

3 "I'll go down to the river and paddle with my friends," thought Piglet. But when he got to the river, there was no one there and the water was very cold.

4 "This is very odd. We've paddled in the river nearly every day this summer," said Piglet. Just then, Pooh came along wearing a woolly jumper.

5 "What's going on, Pooh? All the fun things we've done during the summer don't seem to work any more," cried Piglet.

6 "That's because the summer is over and autumn is just beginning. Now it's time to do some different fun things," explained Pooh.

7 Pooh and Piglet started by having a contest to see who could catch the most falling leaves. "I think I'm going to enjoy the autumn just as much as the summer!" cheered Piglet.

Shadow fun

Help Lumpy to match the shadows with the list of words below. What is on the list but does not appear as a shadow?

skipping rope
Eeyore's tail
scooter
Roo
kite

tennis racket
honey pot
butterfly
flower
watering can
Piglet

Answer: Honey pot

59

Pooh's puzzles

1

Can you find each of the shapes below in the picture?

square   star   triangle   circle   rectangle

2

Which of Pooh's pots have been painted using the same colours?

a   b   c   d   e

Answer: 1. Square = Pooh's blocks, star = on Roo's ball, triangle = Rabbit's carrot on seed label, circle = Roo's ball, rectangle = Rabbit's seed label. 2. b and e.

Arctic Eeyore

1 It was a really chilly day, and Eeyore wasn't feeling very happy. "It's so cold in here that my tail has frozen solid," he shivered.

2 No matter how much Eeyore huddled, the icy wind blew through the cracks in his little house. Just then, Pooh came whizzing along on his sledge.

3 "Poor Eeyore, you look frozen!" said Pooh.
"I don't think donkeys were meant to live in cold places," chattered Eeyore.

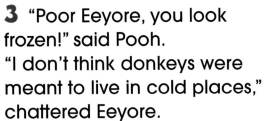

4 "If you were an Arctic donkey, the cold wouldn't bother you at all," said Pooh.
"Why doesn't the cold bother them?" asked Eeyore.

5 "Arctic donkeys have igloos to keep them warm. I hear that they're very cosy!" explained Pooh. "What's an igloo?" puzzled Eeyore.

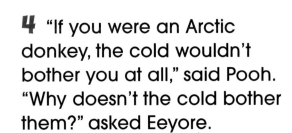

6 "An igloo is a house made of snow!" said Pooh, as he began piling snow against Eeyore's little home. It didn't take Pooh long to completely cover it.

7 The layer of snow kept the cold and wind out of Eeyore's house. The little donkey was soon feeling warm and cosy. "I'm going to pretend I'm an Arctic donkey for the rest of winter," he chuckled.

The special snowman

1 One snowy day, Pooh and Piglet were building a rather handsome snowman. "It's almost finished," giggled Piglet.

2 But suddenly, a sloppy snowball splatted into the snowman and knocked off its head! "A perfect hit!" cheered Tigger.

3 "You ruined our snowman!" sighed Pooh. "Snowmen are built to be knocked over. If I didn't do it they'd only end up melting anyway," chuckled Tigger.

4 Pooh looked around and saw broken snowmen everywhere! Tigger was ruining all the snowmen in the Hundred Acre Wood!

5 "I think we should make a special snowman for Tigger," said Pooh. The friends went to Pooh's house and found two different-sized honey pots.

6 Pooh and Piglet filled the two pots with snow and put the small one on top of the big one. Then they covered the pots to make them look just like a snowman.

7 When Tigger arrived, he threw his snowballs as hard as he could at the solid snowman. But it showed no sign of crumbling. "So, you want to put up a fight, do you?" laughed Tigger.

8 "I think Tigger will be busy for some time," giggled Piglet. "Now everyone can build their snowmen in peace," chuckled Pooh.

Snowman puzzles

a

b

c

d

e

1 Put the snowmen in order, from the tallest to the shortest.

2 Which of these objects did Pooh NOT use on his snowman?

Answers: 1. c, a, d, b, e. 2. The green scarf.